Working across the Boundaries

Experiences of primary health and social care partnerships in practice

Edited by Richard Poxton

King's Fund

Published by
King's Fund Publishing
11–13 Cavendish Square
London W1M 0AN

First published 1999

ISBN 1 85717 262 0

A CIP catalogue record for this book is available from the British Library

Available from:

King's Fund Bookshop
11–13 Cavendish Square
London W1M 0AN

Tel: 0171 307 2591
Fax: 0171 307 2801

This report has been produced to disseminate research findings and promote good practice in health and social care. It has not been professionally copy-edited or proof-read.

Printed and bound in Great Britain

Contents

Working Across the Boundaries

Experiences of primary health and social care partnerships in practice

Introduction

In this collection of stories, six practitioners and managers talk about their experience of working with their counterparts in health and social services in development initiatives that were supported by the King's Fund in the period 1993-98. All of the accounts provide insights into the way people in primary health care and social services worked together before the Labour Government resolved to bring down the "Berlin walls" dividing health and social services. In this respect, these stories about primary health and social care partnerships relate to a period that pre-dates the establishment of Primary Care Groups.

The accounts are given by an interesting cross-section of the health and social care community, including a general practitioner and a social worker, a social services team manager, a director of commissioning from a health authority, a director of social services and a joint commissioning officer employed by a local authority and a health authority. Not surprisingly, they have very different perspectives, influenced by their different roles and responsibilities within the overall health and social care system. These different viewpoints tell us a great deal about how it feels to be working at three different levels in the system. Thus, we hear about initiatives on the frontline where professionals work with individual patients and clients; about experiments in locality commissioning groups focussing on the needs of local populations; and about developments taking place among strategic authorities trying to re-shape services across and boroughs and wider areas.

In the course of telling their stories, the writers reveal their motivation for working in partnership at a time when such collaboration was purely voluntary and, in some respects, an "extra" for busy people who have more than enough to do in their "daytime job". Thus, George Blackburn shows how his experience in child protection led him to apply the same principles of co-ordination and integration to the care of older people, recognising the tragic consequences that can result from failures of different agencies to work together. Alasdair Thomson, a GP, also felt strongly about the importance of tackling the problems of an ageing population by working more closely with social services and community health services. This focus on the needs of vulnerable people is evident in most of the stories but it is also clear that other considerations can come into play, such as the need (on the part of social services) to achieve more appropriate referrals by GPs (Williams).

There are also insights into the power relationships that can facilitate or hinder effective joint working. Thus, we hear how social services staff can sometimes feel that they are not being treated as equal partners by their health service colleagues (Blackburn) and can sometimes feel, initially at least, in awe of GPs (Rogers). In some joint working groups, social services staff can be so outnumbered by GPs and other health colleagues that their presence and contribution appears to be marginalised (Thomson). And Rachel Ayling shows us how people who work up and down the health and social care boundary can sometimes feel powerless when the main players on other side of the divide run into major difficulties.

While these stories are honest about the problems that can arise, they are also very open about the strategies used to forge mutual understanding and respect.

Thus, we hear about the efforts made to build mutual understanding and a shared vision, through informal lunches and structured workshops (Stanwick and Thomson) and committee agendas featuring regular 'information exchange' slots (Williams). There are also examples of new posts being created to help co-ordinate efforts and to manage complex changes (Stanwick, Ayling) and we hear at first hand from people who decided to play leadership or enabler roles in order to progress developments (Stanwick, Williams, Blackburn).

Inevitably, problems arise when people from different professional backgrounds and organisations work together. All six authors talk about their problems. Sometimes, the difficulties are caused by external factors such as re-organisation in the NHS and local government, that seriously set back joint work by disrupting good working relationships that have been built up (Ayling, Thomson, Stanwick). Or the problems can be intrinsic to joint working, where there can be frustrations about the slow pace of change and where even the most enthusiastic activist finds it difficult to maintain momentum (Blackburn, Stanwick)). We also hear about the practical difficulties of engaging GPs in collaboration with social services and the challenge this presents to managers who can only make headway with individual GPs who are committed to working that way.

Perhaps, most poignantly of all, Rachel Ayling's account shows how tensions can build up that can stretch good working relationships almost to breaking point, as when resource pressures cause purchasers to tighten their eligibility criteria or lead to disagreements about lowering the level of investment into particular services.

Despite the problems, none of the authors show any desire to stop working with their health or social services counterparts. At the time of writing, most were beginning to see some real pay-offs that were making all their efforts worthwhile. These pay-offs could involve service developments making life easier for users and carers (Thomson, Williams, Rogers) but there also appears to be real satisfaction in working in new ways and strong hopes for a better future.

No one is complacent about the challenges that remain, whether that means finding better ways to involve users and carers (Thomson) or to make the links between priorities and plans at primary care level and those relating to strategic authorities. What is clear is that all have learned a great deal as they have worked with colleagues across the health and social care divide. Their reflections on the ups and downs of resolving at least some of the old problems makes for an interesting and topical account.

Looking ahead

As we move into a new era where partnership between health and social care has become a policy priority of the Labour Government, the experience and expertise of these practitioners and managers will be invaluable. All of them are continuing to work in health or social services (see 'Where are they now?' pp54-55) contributing to Primary Care Groups, to Health Improvement Programmes and to providing services for people with long term illness or disability.

The experience and expertise they gained in the course of these early primary care and social care experiments will, no doubt, be applied in the new setting. A new policy environment and new organisational arrangements should make co-operation and collaboration easier than it has been in the past. But the stories told here suggest that real success will depend as much on the determination and creativity of practitioners and managers as it will on Government edict and structural change.

The Social Worker's Story

Changing Roles For Practitioners

Jim Rogers
Social Worker,
Knowsley Social Services Department

Jim Rogers is a social worker in the Huyton Adult Care Team. He is an experienced and thoughtful practitioner keen to test out new ways of working whilst always wanting to demonstrate best practice. Knowsley has developed a reputation as a progressive Social Services Department responding imaginatively to continuing social and economic hardships in the area. The leadership style is facilitative, and Jim and his practitioner colleagues have benefited from close support and guidance from centrally based staff. In this chapter he describes what it has been like working with both GPs and district nurses, and how his relatively informal early collaboration has helped pave the way for a full scale alignment of social services staff with GP Practices.

Background

I am a social worker employed by Knowsley Social Services Department on Merseyside. There are 5 adult social work teams in the borough: Huyton, Kirkby, South, Whiston Hospital and Fazakerley Hospital. I am based with the Huyton Adult Team which is the largest team in the borough handling over 2500 referrals between July 1996 and June 1997. The team is generic in Adult Services.

Knowsley, in common with much of Greater Merseyside, has experienced massive socio-economic problems. The problems are long standing and are due, in no small measure, to the remorseless decline or contraction of many staple labour intensive industries, too numerous to mention. As an example, in 1991 only 70% of the Borough's population aged 16-59/64 years were economically active against an average for England and Wales of 77.5%. Only 33% of the total population were in any form of employment, a decrease from 37% in 1981. The average for England and Wales is 44%.

The census returns of 1991 also reveal that male unemployment stood at 27%, more than double the national average as was the unemployment rates for young males aged 18-24 years.

It is in the area of health, linked to deprivation, that the figures become more worrying. The 1991 Census also found that 1-in-6 of Knowsley's residents felt that they had an incapacitation, health problem or long term illness which impaired or restricted their daily activities.

The Borough's Standard Mortality Rate for adults below 65 years show a death rate 27% above the national average. This picture is evident across all the main causes of death. For example, and again using 1991 census returns:

Coronary Heart Disease	39% above national average
Lung Cancer	47% above national average
Respiratory Illnesses	48% above national average

The most recent (1995) estimate of Knowsley's population puts the figure at 156,581. This appears to be a slight increase after a continual loss over the previous 20 years. Figures also reveal the general ageing of the population with increases in the 30-49 and the 60+ age groups. In parallel there is a marked decrease in the number of young adults in the 15-29 age cohort. The ageing population has implications for both social and health care services, particularly as more than half of Knowsley's population aged 60+ live alone.

Working Together For Older People

Services for older people most often provide the trigger for joint working. In "Working Together" Rummery and Glendinning (1997) assert that "it is important not to assume that infirmity is necessarily a consequence of old age. However, the health/social services divide is particularly problematic for frail older people, whose needs are likely to cross organisational boundaries. It is in relation to services for older people that professionals are also likely to experience problems of access and co-ordination." This factor is particularly relevant to me as my caseload comprises predominantly older service users. It was against this backdrop that my involvement in joint working commenced.

The White Paper "Caring for People", which was presented to Parliament in 1989, provided the template for collaborative working between social services and health staff in Knowsley from Autumn 1992 onwards. In my team, there had been a long standing, if nominal, attachment to GPs' practices. However, the National Health Service and Community Care Act 1990 became the catalyst for establishing a separation between the purchase and provision of health and social care. In Knowsley, several multi-disciplinary meetings and discussions were held to formulate a cross agency protocol to meet the challenge of the new community care duties and responsibilities. Many initiatives ensued, including the joint working of social workers and district nurses to monitor the quality of mutual care plans and the 2-year secondment of a social worker to a community health centre to work specifically with dementia referrals.

Of course, the two agencies worked together before that but this was invariably activated by emergencies, followed by crisis intervention and management. Such interventions rarely entailed collaboration on assessment or care planning. It was in recognition of the limited nature of the methods then in use that a Project Plan was formulated to address the situation. It was decided to use that model as a benchmark to develop and inform a more prescribed and integrated arrangement.

Social Work and Primary Care

A multi-disciplinary steering group was set up in June 1995. The group comprised myself and 2 social work colleagues, our team manager, clinical supervisors representing the community district nurses team, together with managers and research staff from health and social services. The group's remit was to implement the attachment of 3 identified social workers to 4 GP practices for a 6-month period in the Huyton Adult Team area. The project was to be evaluated at the end of the period. If the evaluation was to be positive it would be open to discussion to see if the attachment arrangement could be rolled out to the whole locality area.

The project objective was the integration of social workers within primary health care teams to enable :

- early and positive intervention, reducing the need for crisis intervention.

- appropriate and timely assessment ... provision of high quality care subject to regular review and audit.

- named social workers working with named district nurses and primary health care teams to facilitate improved communications.

- clarification of roles and responsibilities and organisation to improve referral processes.

- improvement of the interface between the hospital social worker, assessment team and community workers.

- the exploration of improving links with neighbouring Local Authority Social Services Departments.

The project was thus christened SWAP - Social Workers Attached to Practices, and was scheduled to run from September 1995 to March 1996.

The aims and objectives of the project were defined to GPs in the locality area and four volunteered to participate in the project. My two colleagues and I were attached to the four practices on the basis of the number of existing service users known to be registered with the practices. I was allocated two practices; a single handed practice and a practice with four GPs. The latter practice became one of five national development sites working with the King's Fund.

I found the preparatory work of the Steering Group immensely interesting. I must also admit that I joined the group with all of my presumptions, assumptions and stereotypes fully intact. My personal attitude towards GPs hovered somewhere between subservience and downright obsequiousness. If directed by my GP to stand on my head in a corner, my probable response would have been "which corner?".

I say this in a light hearted way but, more seriously, the social services staff in the group were concerned as to how our new GP colleagues would view us in collaborative arrangements. We were wary of the "professional tribalism" which has been reported all too frequently. From a social services perspective my colleagues operated in a social work team with a devolved budget. We were also mindful of the fact that our new health colleagues would be as cost conscious as we were. We were both, in effect, custodians of our respective budgets. This was a salient factor as the project had to be achieved within existing resource levels. In the discussion stage, we invented scenarios where finance might be an issue. I am happy to relate that, in my experience at least, finance was never a matter of dispute. A happy by-product for me is that I am now more assertive and proactive with my own GP ...... sometimes!

In the run up to the commencement of the project I made several visits to my 2 practices. On these visits, I was either accompanied by managerial colleagues or solo. These visits were invaluable in enabling us to get to know one another and also to outline our distinctive roles and functions. As a purchaser and a provider it also enabled me to explain Knowsley Social Services Department's eligibility criteria and charging policy. This was crucial as Rummery and Glendinning outline, "Boundary problems between health and social services are made more acute by the fact that the former remain free at the point of use; both domiciliary and residential care provided through social services departments (including nursing home care) are subject to means tested charges".

This contact was an invaluable precursor to what was to become an extremely fulfilling working relationship. But I realised that I had pushed my luck when I went for the sympathy vote and tried to describe the mountain of paperwork that the modern care manager has to deal with. I sensed a collective glazing of the eyes.

I was fortunate that the two practices I was attached to were both serviced by the same district nurse team. This was invaluable in terms of collaborative continuity. The district nurses were to become a constant in most referrals.

As mentioned, the project was intended to run from September 1995 to March 1996. For myself and a colleague, the project had been highly successful and we continued with our attachments. Sadly, the experience of my third colleague was not as positive and this attachment formally ceased.

Securing Better Outcomes

My attachments continue to be positive and fruitful. Unsurprisingly the two practices are run on totally different lines. This is a huge bonus to me as it allows my contact to be flexible. In both practices, I was immediately integrated into their team working. As stated, this was aided by the fact that both practices had the same district nurse teams - which was an added bonus for me. This co-terminosity is most positive as it means that we work with the same users and carers. Joint working thus produces shared records, case history and experience.

I realised the importance of this aspect quite literally in the first week of the Project. A gentleman was referred to me by the District Nurses' Department. He was in his late 80's, extremely frail, in declining health, being cared for by his wife of similar age, who herself presented evidence of dementia. They were a fiercely independent couple who were known to our Department mainly for refusing services. Their family were now desperately concerned about them, their independence notwithstanding. This case was to forge our embryonic joint working arrangement in a most positive way.

To do justice to our intervention would require a comprehensive Case Study which sadly space prevents. Suffice to say that our joint involvement lasted close on 2 years. The main players in maintaining this gentleman in the community were the District Nurses' Department and our Department.

The couple received a wide range of health and social services including home care (provided by both the Local Authority and private agencies), aids, specialist nursing services, respite and, eventually, long term care. It was true collaborative working, constantly responding to ever changing needs and settings (home, hospitals, surgery and nursing home). For my colleagues and I, it was our most complex case at the time, involving, quite often, complex family dynamics.

Difficult as the case was I am proud of our work with this couple. Our joint working ensured that our interventions, often responding to crises, were dual, synchronised and thereby more effective. Given our shared knowledge of the minutiae of the case we could better inform and involve our co-workers; in my case, all community care providers and in the case of my district nurse colleagues, medical and nursing services. This latter point was critical in hospital admission and discharge arrangements.

Sadly, the gentleman died in early 1997 just after entering long term care. I take it as a tribute to our joint working that he was able to remain at home, with support from health and social services, for as long as he did. He was survived by his wife whose dementia subsequently became more pronounced and she received a range of support services.

Forming Closer Relationships

In the two years since my attachments, a mutually supportive professional culture has evolved. We have developed a way of working which we feel is beneficial to our service users/patients and ourselves. The secret of this productive working relationship was incredibly simple - face-to-face contact. No more was the social worker just a voice at the other end of a telephone. Personal contact also improved the quality of a referral. There were hiccups, without doubt, but our way of working enabled us to promptly address any problems or areas of concern.

I mentioned earlier the differences between the two practices that I was attached to. One is a single handed practice where I visit as and when and in addition attend scheduled PHCT meetings. In this practice, I have marginally more contact with the GP than other team members do.

My other practice is much larger: 4 GPs with associated administration and reception staff. Here I have the use of an office/treatment room which is used by all the attached staff (district nurses, health visitors, chiropodist etc.) - not at the same time thankfully! My allotted time is Tuesday afternoons when I receive visitors, at present mostly other professionals. And I still get a kick when a GP knocks on the door and I get the chance to say "Come in"!

But in truth, such contact is critical in putting flesh on a referral. I am convinced that the quality of referrals has improved by that simple device. It has certainly been exceedingly beneficial to me as there are opportunities for discussion and shared information.

Early on, my major point of contact was with the District Nurses' Department but, over time, there has been as much contact with GPs as with district nurses – something which I regard as positive.

Another benefit of this relationship is that it has improved my understanding of the roles and functions of my health colleagues. Given that an integral element of the whole project was sharing, I trust that they are now more fully informed about my practice. I feel that what I do has in turn been broadened. Any professional tribalism which may have been evident when we began working together has disappeared totally.

Moving Ahead - Towards Aligned Care Teams

What of the future? On the macro level, the discussions on joint commissioning between Knowsley Social Services Department and St. Helens and Knowsley Health Authority continue apace. This is obviously crucially important and many joint initiatives will be awaiting the outcome. For instance, I would like to explore the feasibility of a joint funded service to meet those needs that don't fall within the remit of either health or social services, perhaps something based on the model of the Wiltshire Handy Helps Scheme.

On a local level, and as a direct consequence of the SWAP Project, new teams are being proposed for Huyton. The aim is to bring GP practices, social workers, district nurses and possibly home care staff together in teams to serve the health and social care needs of the same adult population. It is proposed that these teams will in effect be joint primary health/social services teams providing a single access point to core services, including assessment for community care and community nursing services and onward referral to specialist health and social care. It is hoped that other agencies such as Housing and the Benefits Agency will also provide some input to the teams.

Each team will be required to agree a protocol for referrals, criteria for joint visits and feedback and shared information. The objective is to develop co-ordinated, multi-disciplinary assessments, care planning and service provision. The amount of time other staff will spend at GP Practices will depend upon space availability and the like. Though at the discussion stage the model looks flexible and exciting: very much the logical conclusion of the work that my colleagues and I have been involved in as it intends to encompass shared documentation and records and, most interestingly, budget alignment.

I have been involved in early discussions and am excited at the prospect given my experience to date of joint working. However, much work still needs to be done at a level many rungs higher than my level. Nonetheless, I am confident that these proposals will become fact. As soon as the template has been formulated I expect true joint commissioning to follow as a matter of course.

In proposing the new teams, the steering group comprising managers from St. Helens and Knowsley Health, St. Helens and Knowsley Community Health (NHS) Trust and Knowsley Social Services Department conclude that:

"Our experience in Huyton already shows that referrals by primary care staff to Social Services are more appropriate; referrals are dealt with more quickly; joint visits happen when appropriate. Overall patients/service users have received a more accessible, more co-ordinated service. This avoids duplication and ensures the best use of resources."

References

Rummery K, Glendenning C *"Working Together". Primary Care Involvement in Commissioning Social Care Services.* The National Primary Care Research and Development Centre, Manchester 1997.

Knowsley Social Services Department and St. Helens and Knowsley Health *"Social Workers Attached to Practices Project Report".* 1996

The GP's Story

Developing Community Partnerships From a Practice Base

Alasdair Thomson GP
Chief Executive,
Dartford, Gravesham & Swanley Healthcare Partnerships Project

Alasdair Thomson is a General Practitioner in Swanscombe, West Kent and is also Chief Executive of the locality Heatlhcare Partnerships Project, which is in the process of transforming into a Primary Care Group. He is one of a group of GPs in Dartford and Gravesham with a longstanding interest in influencing decisions through partnership, initially with the Health Authority and more recently with Social Services. He firmly believes in respecting and developing the contributions of all participants, whether looking at individual patients' needs or those of the locality. Here he examines how local pilots were set up to improve services for older people through collaboration at Practice level, paying particular attention to the role of the GP and possible implications for the future.

Introduction

There has always been some semblance of joint working between primary care and social services. However, the depth of commitment has never really progressed further than a "stand-offish" sort of acceptance of each other. Invariably, the joint working has usually been associated with crisis management, leading to a sometimes acrimonious debate over the definition of "urgent". Other initiatives to improve joint working have tended to founder due to lack of resources.

As a general practitioner, it is clear to me that a closer relationship between health and social services is essential if we are to seriously tackle the issues around the ageing population which we invariably have to serve. Health (or ill-health) is closely linked to social well-being and vice versa.

From this perspective, it is difficult to argue against joint commissioning at primary care level, as the means by which care can be delivered, efficiently and cost effectively.

Dartford, Gravesham & Swanley Locality

The locality is situated to the south and east of Greater London, bounded by the south bank of the River Thames and is largely made up of the urban areas of Dartford, Gravesham and Swanley towns, together with smaller rural areas to the south. The locality is a constituent part of West Kent Health Authority (WKHA) and the primary healthcare of the population of 220,000 is served by 114 GPs, arranged in 37 Practices, of which 15 are single-handed. Currently, Social Services provision is on a patch as opposed to a practice basis.

There is a wide variation in deprivation scores in the locality, with a (not unexpected) corresponding variation in health needs. Townsend scores illustrate that Gravesham (+6) is the most deprived area in West Kent, whilst rural parts of Gravesham Borough (-6) are the least deprived.

Not surprisingly, there are significant levels of unemployment, as the traditional heavy industries such as cement and paper making have all but disappeared.

There is a significant ethnic minority population, particularly in Gravesend, giving rise to specific health and social needs.

Swanscombe Practice is one of four sites within the locality, which has piloted joint commissioning of elderly services at practice level. The Group Practice consists of 4 GPs, serving a population of 8,300. In addition to the GPs, the Primary Healthcare Team consists of a full-time practice manager, ancillary staff, practice nurse and attached district nursing and health visiting staff.

Developing Local Partnerships

The new Health Authorities, established in April 1996, were given a clear role to develop a "Primary Care-led NHS". In West Kent, this led to the development of Joint Commissioning Groups (JCG) in each of the four localities. The JCGs consisted of Fundholding and non-Fundholding GPs and Health Authority Commissioning Managers. We quickly established a proactive approach to commissioning community based healthcare provision. However, it soon became evident that a "pure" health based approach to commissioning community healthcare would not solve problems around social care needs and the requirement for social services input. Therefore, it seemed logical to extend the joint commissioning approach to involve health and social services in a "Community Partnership" (COMPART), project which was supported and evaluated by the King's Fund.

A successful exploratory workshop was held, involving the Community Trust (district nurses, health visitors, physiotherapists), the Acute Geriatric Service, Primary Healthcare Teams (GPs, practice nurses, practice managers), the Health Authority, Social Services (care managers, OTs) the CHC and voluntary organisations. A main outcome was that COMPART subsequently developed two strands:-

- A "top-down" approach to developing mental health services which involved pooling of the fundholder and non-fundholder budgets for mental health provision

- A "bottom-up" approach to developing provision for older people at GP Practice level.

Within the Locality, the Practice based sites reflected the varying aspects of GP commissioning and purchasing as they then stood:

- non-fundholder

- fundholder

- two fundholder/non-fundholder groups

In total, the population coverage was 48,500.

The Practice based work programme was co-ordinated by the COMPART Project Board, which in turn reported to the newly constituted Locality Commissioning Pilot (under EL(97)37), known as the Dartford, Gravesham & Swanley Healthcare Partnerships Project (D&G HCPP).

Locality Work Programme

The initial and subsequent workshops highlighted a number of "burning issues" which were seen to be common to all Practices and also to Health and Social Services:

- Joint assessment of individual health and social care needs

- Hospital discharge arrangements

- Community equipment and Occupational Therapy

- Alternatives to hospital admission

The overarching aim of the project, agreed by all participants, was to improve service delivery (health and social care) for the benefit of the older population. The participating Practices would develop their own models to address the problems, which could then be rolled out to all GP Practices in the locality.

Early Problems

There were several, potentially serious, early problems; and with hindsight, these can be traced back to mistakes in the design of the project plan. In fact, there was, initially, a clear lack of a robust plan at Practice level and hence the inability to cope with early setbacks. This lack of planning can be attributed to the enthusiasm of the "players" at ground level who clearly wanted to get on with putting ideas into practice. The enthusiasm was not the problem, but the consequence of not fulfilling early aspirations could well have resulted in disillusionment.

The early problems were:-

a)   Organisational differences

b)   Unrealistic goals

c)   Failures in "Player-Manager" (vertical) linkages

a)   There are clear differences in the structure and culture of health and social services organisations. From my (health) perspective, this is not meant as a criticism of Social Services, but is simply a recognition that problems are necessarily tackled in different ways. It is also obvious that the COMPART project was "health dominated" in terms of the organisational background of the majority of the "players". Furthermore, there were no established close formal working arrangements between practice staff and care managers. This was mainly due to the fact that social services staff worked across several practices in a geographical patch. Therefore, it was recognised that reorganisation at care manager level had to be treated sensitively, even though there was a mandate to do so. However, a more significant threat to the project arose when Kent Social Services had to undergo a county-wide reorganisation in response to changes in local government structure

In terms of the project timescale, the impact of these pressures was significant; although the team players at practice level had been identified some four months into the project, there followed a six month period of uncertainty. Once this uncertainty had been largely resolved issues still remained over just how close the integration could be; for example, could Care Managers be physically based in the Practice (which could, of course, lead to problems over information sharing)?.

b)   It had been relatively easy to identify the service problems which I have previously mentioned. By their very nature, and also because they were long standing, solutions were unlikely to be simple. At the outset, the size of the task was not fully appreciated by the individual sites. The problems were identified and expressed clearly enough, but, with hindsight, the aims and objectives were not clearly defined. This led to unrealistic expectations of achievements and timescales. Perhaps the major factor that was forgotten was that all individuals involved in the project had plenty of other work (and priorities) to do at the same time as developing joint commissioning.

c)   Partly because of the organisational difficulties already discussed, the early stages saw the Practice sites working in some degree of isolation. There was also uncertainty, particularly amongst the Community Trust employees (district nurses and health visitors) and care managers, over the handling of possible conflicts between the demands of the project and those of the Trust (most likely to be expressed through their line management).

Achievements

Perhaps the greatest achievement to date has been that all the Practice based teams are still intact and the original enthusiasm to improve services for older people at the point of delivery is very much in evidence. Above all, the early experiences have served to highlight mistakes, which have then been used as valuable learning exercises. The important links are in place and they act as a secure base for future success.

The COMPART Project Board

The Board consists of representatives from the pilot sites and senior managers (from HCPP, WKHA, Social Services & Thameslink Community Trust). The Board is the link between "players" and managers. Despite the early problems the Board has maintained its focus on supporting major change at operational and strategic levels.

Working together

From a base of little or no joint working, the Practice sites have been successful in bringing about horizontal integration. This has developed through mutual respect and understanding of each other's roles and responsibilities. It has also highlighted areas where there are overlapping working arrangements, which would be targets for joint commissioning and, ultimately, joint purchasing.

Re-stating the Objectives

The four main areas of work are as stated previously. They are now recognised as being major pieces of work, which are likely to have implications, in time, for the whole of the locality. It has been decided that each site should concentrate on one of the main objectives.

Other less formal objectives would be pursued at practice site level, as appropriate. Therefore at my site, we decided to concentrate on joint assessments, but also continued to develop our own older population needs database. This new approach has proven to be much more successful, and now, a clearer picture of what needs to be done is emerging through a more robust project plan.

Involving-Users and Carers

The direct involvement of the service users and their carers is an integral part of the COMPART project. There is considerable debate as to how they can be involved effectively. However dialogue with the voluntary organisations has begun. for example, at our site we have sought help and involvement from 'Crossroads'.

Joint Assessment

The current arrangements for assessing health and social care requirements of older people would seem to epitomise the 'Berlin wall' culture which exists between health and social services. Having to carry out two assessments on the same patient results in confusion for the individual (who may have to pay a contribution for some or all care input), an overlap of staff roles and, very often, arguments as to who is paying.

Joint assessment would seem to address the issue of overlapping roles, leading to joint working arrangements and indeed there is no shortage of appropriate paperwork. However, from a joint commissioning (and purchasing) perspective, the objective must be to develop a method for agreeing a joint budget. A process for achieving this is now underway; the key people involved are the district nurse and care manager who are currently agreeing common principles with the Health Authority as budget holder. It is important to remember that the outcome of the joint assessments (in terms of health or social services input) will still be dependent on the availability of cash-limited resources.

Joint Commissioning and the GP

From the GP's point of view, joint commissioning could be seen as either a threat or an opportunity. To the "old style" GP (as reactive or ill-health interventionist) the former applies, but the reactive response is unlikely to be sustainable as a model for the future. However, the pro-active role of the GP as health and welfare promoter is gradually being developed. If services are to be planned appropriately then the GP's role must change to acknowledge to a much greater extent the input of other members of the PHCT.

Using the development of a joint assessment protocol as an example, the GP can be both "player" and "manager". As player there is a requirement to assess the medical history and, based upon this, give a prognosis which will influence the individual's care package. As manager (assuming that the GP is seen as leader of the PHCT) delegation of the decision making process (i.e. of what constitutes the most appropriate care package) to other members of the PHCT will encourage and improve working relationships within the team. It is this approach to joint commissioning which I am promoting in our project. Personally, I have found it fairly easy to accept this approach and I believe other GPs involved in different aspects of the project are of a similar persuasion. It is to the credit of our partners that they have also taken on board the principles of joint commissioning. It should be noted that GPs often have difficulty in delegating, which stems from their 24 hour responsibility to their patients. Of course, this philosophy will not be universally embraced unless there are tangible benefits for both the patient and the GP; hence an evolutionary process rather than a revolutionary one.

The Future

The concept of a primary care-led NHS is now well accepted at both strategic and operational levels. However, putting ideas into practice has proved to be more problematic. Evidence of success from total purchasing projects and from fundholding has been mixed. Where there has been success, it has generally been in community services and where there has been a high level of collaboration between the parties.

The COMPART project has built on the developing joint commissioning networks within the locality and the inclusion of Social Services is in keeping with current political thinking on breaking down barriers between health and social care.

The important building blocks for the future are now in place :

- the links between operational and strategic levels

- putting the patient (and carer) first

- shared values

- a multi-disciplinary approach to problem solving

- the application of different (Practice specific) solutions to similar problems

- an incremental approach to change rather than "big bang"

- a tacit agreement to devolve a shared budget to Practice level (with appropriate safeguards)

- appreciating the Practice position relative to the "bigger (locality) picture'

Therefore, success will be measured on our ability to deliver:

- clear benefits in health and social care delivery for older people in the community

- movement from joint working to joint commissioning and purchasing

- agreed priorities which have a clear locality focus

- increasing user and carer involvement

- the ability to apply models of care to a wider group, namely the locality Social Services being physically based in the primary care setting and so moving to, for example, common records and open record keeping.

Conclusions

In this chapter I have attempted to illustrate the impact of joint commissioning, from my perspective as a GP. The thread which is common to both purchasers and providers is that of ensuring an improved service for patients. However it is clear that service provision has to be carefully managed within a cash-limited budget. As a consequence, we have to be alert to issues of cost-effectiveness and value for money, however unpalatable that may seem.

Although the project is in its infancy, there are already benefits for the Practice; the roles of members of the Primary Healthcare Team have become clearer and, for the first time, a sustainable relationship with Social Services has emerged. There is a base for joint working, which can now be further developed into a joint commissioning framework.

The Practice will gradually build a meaningful profile of older people's care needs which can be used to forecast future as well as current needs.

It is also conceivable that the GP's role will also change, gradually moving away from having to oversee (often only to 'rubber stamp') the decisions of others, to giving medical advice and treatment when appropriate.

Despite some initial setbacks, which caused concern at operational level, there is now a renewed optimism that work can move forward.

The Social Services Team Manager's Story

Towards an Integrated Health and Social Care Team

George Blackburn
Adult Care Team Manager,
Wiltshire Social Services Department

George Blackburn has been at the heart of health and social care collaboration in Trowbridge for five years. During this time he has experienced both the highs and lows involved in moving towards an integrated system of primary care. He would be the first to acknowledge the important contribution made by others at agency level and "on the ground". But this is very much George's personal account, told with the benefit of significant experience and an outlook which at times manages to combine both the optimistic and the suspicious. He relates the experiences so far and speculates on the fundamental implications for the way in which Social Services are accessed locally.

Introduction

This is a description of a professional journey : events from November 1993 to the present during which I have been working to try to develop new services that will bring tangible benefits to older people. I want to convey not just the cold facts but something of what I have personally experienced and learnt. I have found it an exhilarating experience, at times both time consuming and taxing. It is important to note that I am not a "development worker" and that the sort of developments described are inevitably a lower priority than my day to day team management work. My job is to manage the Trowbridge Adult Care Team, a complex enough activity in itself without trying to re-invent the local health and social care system at the same time!

Personal Experience of Partnership Working

In the early 1980's I was a Level 3 social worker in a Child Protection Team on Merseyside. A crystal-clear memory from that time was related to "partnership" with other agencies. It was absolutely imperative in child protection work to work in tandem with the child's health visitor, who we knew would have the ear of the GP. In our small team in the Wirral we had a very firmly held belief in one worker taking responsibility for co-ordination of care activity to the family. We called it "case management" and it was almost always the province of the social worker. (Incidentally it was this experience that taught me how much "management" is involved in good social work practice and how particularly suited *good* social workers are to what we now call care management). Good social workers in my view take overall responsibility for *managing* the health and social care input to their clients. They should make it their business to be aware, like any manager, of the overall picture, and use their skills to "pull the strings". When social workers adopt this role, which they have to negotiate, they provide an invaluable function which other professionals look to them to carry out.

Following from that came the notion of regular, informal meetings of the professional staff involved with the family which we called "network" meetings. The communication had to be tight and clear. Our specialist team had been set up in response to the tragic death of an abused child and we were determined to ensure that there would be no repetition.

When I moved to Trowbridge in 1991 my working culture and professional instincts were that partnerships work, that they are essential to good practice and that *it is necessary to invest time and energy in the building of partnerships*. The same basic principles I had applied to working with abused children were those I brought to bear in adult care work :

- working in partnership establishes who is responsible for what

- being part of a multi-agency network which meets regularly establishes clarity of objectives

My Local Area: Trowbridge

Trowbridge is a small market town in Wiltshire. It is the county town of Wiltshire and has a population of approximately 37,000 people. Its very ordinariness is in fact highly significant in that there would appear to be no particular reason why what can happen in Trowbridge can't happen in other ordinary places. It is certainly not an affluent town: boarded-up shops and some quite large public housing schemes exist and employment is slightly lower than the national average.

However, Trowbridge is different in three aspects of health provision. Firstly, it has a small local hospital which is a source of pride to its citizens and which has survived various attempts to "kill it off" by the health authority. Secondly, all four GP Practices in the town are fundholders. Thirdly two of those GP Practices are total fundholders i.e. they hold the budget for all medical provision for their patients. Also both of these practices, Lovemead and Adcroft, chose to pilot Total Fundholding at the very outset and thereby signalled their ambition to be at the forefront, to be innovative and to become independent from the centralised control of the health authority.

One final piece of context is that from April 1993 my team, somewhat similarly to the GP Practices, became in essence a fundholding team. Almost overnight I became responsible for a community care budget of £408,000 with which to fund all private nursing and residential care placements plus care packages from private agencies. I also became responsible for deployment of staff and was given a budget of £400,000 to pay the existing staffing complement of social workers and OTs and their assistants and linkworkers. This required all the professional staff in my team to experience a new culture and some changes in their working practice.

Developing the Project

In November 1993 Trowbridge was selected as one of the development sites for the first King's Fund Joint Commissioning Project. The aim was to "jointly commission" services for older people with two fund-holding practices in the town. An opportunity to produce a new excellent service, in partnership with Health and utilising additional extra monies, seemed an exciting challenge.

A series of meetings with the two Practices ensued, in fact with two practice managers and one or two GPs. We were joined by strategists from the Social Services Department and the then Health Commission. We all attempted to understand three new terminologies: Kings Fund joint commissioning-speak, GP fundholding health-speak, and social services and Health Commission strategy-speak.

I think it might have been helpful if one person had been responsible for interpreting each other's terminology and ensuring that communication actually occurred. I think we were all guilty of pretending that we understood each other. Also we were guilty of retreating into our "comfort zones" of expertise, secure in the knowledge that we could be authoritative without the danger of anybody else really knowing what we were talking about!

Ultimately the "partnership" fell apart in acrimony. Words were exchanged and both Practices pulled out, one encouraged by the other. I believe that Social Services was conveniently regarded by the Practices as the "guilty party" and that this was orchestrated by both practice managers wishing to deflect blame. I perceived this development as the Social Services being shoe-horned into its traditional role as "incompetent victim" when the going got tough. But I was clear that a line had to be drawn. Until the Practices learned to treat our work with respect, there could be no real partnership and no joint commissioning. A rift was better than being second class citizens in a so-called partnership. But at the same time all the day to day work of the three organisations had to continue as before.

The Lovemead Practice has the largest number of patients in Trowbridge but had not initially been asked to join the project. I was more determined after our initial setback and we approached Lovemead and asked them to join the project. Of course joint suspicion was almost running down the walls but two GPs came forward, showing respect, courtesy and an interest in developing new services. One of the GPs and myself achieved a definite mutual respect : we had both done considerable work in the child protection field and understood very clearly the need for partnership. He also had an understanding and some respect for our work and I was learning about the pressures on GPs. In retrospect the other two Practices in my view made a mistake in not nominating a GP to lead the work with us. Instead the Practice Managers, who appeared to have virtually no understanding of the Social Services Department's work, undertook this role at the same time as various other responsibilities.

To be candid, I suspect that Lovemead believed they could run Community Care much more efficiently than ourselves. But through time and experience this perception disappeared. Early on I made it quite clear that although we might re-arrange our staff deployment, we were not intending to allocate to Lovemead their share of our community care budget. In some ways, however, the various prejudices and preconceptions we had about each other's organisations were fading away.

Looking at Needs

How we went about our collaborative effort has been well documented elsewhere (Henry and Gaskin, 1997[1]). For the needs assessment part suffice to say that it took a long time to understand the requirements to consult widely. It seemed manifestly clear to myself and the GP that we knew the needs already, and I am afraid to say that we learned only through experience that a wide consultation with and about older people could in fact be an enlightening course of action. Three meetings were held of representatives of organisations providing services to older people and a management steering group emerged. I certainly valued the common-sense, practical and experiential comments from the user and carer members. And having consulted, they couldn't be ignored.

I found this a very empowering experience despite encountering some "project -fatigue" by this stage. The work was so time-consuming and the progress seemed so slow. Also, it was like walking in a mine-field, such were the different sensitivities of various parties. The appointment of a development worker was of some relief.

After another large round of consultations with users and carers and professional bodies, a somewhat predictable set of conclusions emerged : that affordable and flexible domestic help, user friendly public transport and a much better information service were all unmet needs of the older population of Trowbridge. What also emerged was a sense of perplexity from users and carers that all the information about access to services for older people stemmed from a large variety of uncoordinated and differently funded organisations. So why couldn't the project re-organise services for older people in Trowbridge that were more "user-friendly", through "one door" without "boundary disputes" as well as trying to do something about the other three issues? In my view the former was more achievable and we decided to focus on re-organising and integrating existing health and social care services in the town.

Support from Senior Management

My immediate ambition was to create an integrated health and social care team at Lovemead Surgery. I was encouraged in this primarily by our Social Services Director, whose writings and conversations on the subject seemed eminently sensible, and also by articles and papers from the Department of Health such as "A Primary Care led National Health Service" which promoted the notion of the GP Practice as the community's centre for health and social care. In addition, it was very important to have the support of my own line manager even though the integration of health and social care was not a high priority for his workload.

---

[1] **Henry, S and Gaskin, L** *The Trowbridge Experience: Care in the community for elderly people* in **Meads, G** *Health and Social Services in Primary Care* FT Healthcare 1997

Developing Relations with Lovemead Surgery

In order to demonstrate how the integrated health and social care team developed I need to describe some important ingredients of that partnership as follows:

a)   **Link Workers**

Wiltshire's "link worker" scheme has been written about extensively so I need not describe it here. It is important here to note that Lovemead benefited from having a link worker with a high degree of pragmatism and determination and that it was one of only two practices in the county to have a post of link worker assistant. This was a post I created amidst some degree of scepticism. The original idea in 1994 was that the assistants would provide practical (and moral) support to the link worker and that they would between them form the embryo of a social care team within the practice at Lovemead. They are both district nurse trained but carry out all the normal functions of an adult care social worker(or assistant). And they are undoubtedly a quick two way communication system between ourselves and the Practice.

b)   **GPs**

Relations between myself and the senior partner remain uniquely positive. He has much regard for the work that we do, and I know that his enthusiasm for integration has led to some considerable strain between himself and his GP colleagues who periodically experience "innovation fatigue", no doubt bolstered by prejudices and preconceptions about Social Services Department staff. I should add that some social services staff also harbour the same lack of understanding of the work pressures on primary health care staff, including GPs.

c)   **Business Manager**

As a champion of primary care purchasing she has been very keen on the idea of the Practice being the community's centre for both health and social care. She also has a conviction that social care would be better organised and funded from the Practice, and so has gradually become more and more receptive to the idea of an integrated health and social care team. Once the decision was made that the development of an integrated team was a definite intention the whole Practice had to be won over and in essence we needed to have a formal invitation to join their business. The Business Manager was invaluable in enabling this to happen. Also, a series of meetings culminating in a presentation to the GPs by our practitioners of the type of work the Adult Care Team carries out was an important determining factor.

Implementing the Integrated Team

The next step involved specific tasks for me and my colleagues:

- Identification of an appropriate proportion of my team to devote to Lovemead, ensuring equity, good skill and personality mix and positive attitudes : the basic method was to apportion a part of the team's staffing resources in correlation with the percentage of Trowbridge patients on Lovemead's books.

- Identification of a similar proportion of the Primary Health Care Team, including their management from Bath and Wiltshire Health Care Trust: this involved close working with the Trust manager, who was extremely positive and able to steer primary health care staff in an integrated direction.

- Setting up team building exercises respecting difference, learning from each other and discarding bureaucratic practices which "got in the way"; my assistant manager was very much involved initially in setting up weekly meetings of the new team and helping them get to grips with each other's practice.

- Identification of finance and an appropriate training person to carry this out - ultimately an outside training consultant was needed to provide the neutrality that was essential and Kings Fund money to fund this was freed up by the development worker.

- Identification of a co-ordinator capable of ironing out all the practicalities : it was important that this role was not provided by an existing manager from either organisation, and ultimately the teams themselves opted for the development worker to carry out this important function.

Relations within my own Team

Once the Social Services Department component of the integrated team had been identified (a process not without its sensitivities) there remained the difficult job of informing, explaining and winning over the rest of the team - clearly they were already aware of what was being proposed. Below is a chart explaining the structure of Trowbridge Adult Care Team in March 1995, with the Lovemead staff underlined.

Social Workers		Link Workers	Occupational Therapists	
JP	30 hrs	JH 30hrs	HC	30hrs
BY	F/T	(already Practice based)	AB	30hrs
SN	½ T			

Social Work Assistants		Link Worker Assistants	Occupational Therapy Assistants	
JC	½ T	AS ½ T	PC	F/T
BC	30hrs	(already Practice based)	(½ based in Practice)	

By January 1997 the Practice had earmarked a room for the integrated team which now comprised the above indicated social services staff, two district nurses, a patient care liaison nurse, a practice nurse and administrative staff. A simple but profound truth was confirmed to me when I sat in on one of their weekly meetings to discuss the patients/clients they had in common, namely that partnership works! The strong team culture of the Social Services Department was wedded to the no-nonsense practical decision making of Health. Nobody needed to be threatened by each other, nobody was being forced to do another colleague's job and the simple fact of sitting together in close proximity helped the team to work together.

The social services straff retained their desks at County Hall pending evaluation, and the rest of my team still regards the Lovemead group as integral to themselves. It is clear, however, that this state of affairs cannot remain indefinitely. Fortunately I am supported by my management in having the autonomy to choose the right time to make the definite and final move.

Trowbridge as a whole

I am determined to develop the integration of health and social care in Trowbridge. Far from feeling a "poor relation" in the health and social care field, I find that from a Social Services Department standpoint I am able to exert considerable influence. After all, there are four Practices and only one Social Services Department team, and I am in a position to understand the culture of each Practice.

I have now aligned the rest of our staff with the three other Practices. What would be obvious to an outside onlooker, and what I have always felt and suspected has been borne out by experience. The Health Service, whether the Trust at Trowbridge Hospital or primary care at the Practices, finds our work invaluable and absolutely relies on our staff to provide the community care that their patients need. Consequently, Health are going to get better outcomes for their patients if they treat us as respected partners and similarly for our staff with Health. Integrated working is now developing well from all Practices.

Looking Ahead

The changes so far in working practices raise a number of issues around what else should change as a consequence. It is no longer clear that well-established social services notions such as the duty system and referrals are either desirable or sustainable in the new regime. The key question, of course, is what makes most sense and is most effective for our service users - users whom we now "share" with the Practices.

It is also clear to me that management across primary health and social care in Trowbridge (and elsewhere) needs to be redefined. The difference in cultures between the supervision of social services staff and the largely stand alone nature of health practitioners becomes very evident when the two operate side by side. There is a good deal of the social services way which I am sure that we should retain, and maybe health services might learn from it (aspects of proper care management, for example) but inevitably the way the quality of the Adult Care Team is assured will continue to develop. At present the Lovemead Health and Social Care Team has three management structures responsible for it: Health Trust, Social Services and the Practice. To make the team pull together with agreed objectives require a major effort of goodwill between the three managers involved. At the end of the day I only have authority over a proportion of the team and while at present, with enthusiasm and commitment, the team functions effectively something relatively trivial (e.g. a personality clash) could make the situation unmanageable.

Community care management is a peculiarly complex matter, not least because the charging policies are so intricate. In my experience, Health Trust practitioners and managers almost have an aversion to this aspect of the work, alien as it is to their culture and training. Therefore, I would argue that the expertise and experience in this field accrued by managers like myself should be utilised in any integrated care scenario.

However, I am sure that further changes will be required until we have become properly integrated from the user's point of view. It is important that we at Practice level continue to make efforts here regardless of what further changes in the organisational structures flow from the NHS White Paper and other important documents. From our experience to date we know that change takes time and can be difficult, but that it can also be rewarding for both users and staff.

Conclusion

The story is, of course, a continuing one and further changes will undoubtedly build upon those I have described here. In describing events I am conscious that a good deal of detail has been omitted. But I would like to emphasise the support I have received from my local management and development colleagues, from Social Services Headquarters, and from our local and national development consultants.

I take the view that Social Services have been given the lead role in Community Care. As a team manager I have taken a leadership role, sometimes from the front, sometimes in the background. I believe that Social Services Department team managers are crucial players in the development of integrated working. They can develop, they can stall, or they can obstruct. I have taken the first road and would recommend it to others.

The Health Authority Commissioner's Story

Learning to Work in Partnership

Stephanie Stanwick
Director of Commissioning (North),
West Kent Health Authority

Stephanie Stanwick has been at the forefront of West Kent Health Authority's partnership activities, working with GPs, local Trusts and Kent Social Services Department.. As Director of Commissioning she is involved in much of the developmental activity in North West Kent as well as ensuring that the core health services continue to function effectively. She displays the range of leadership skills necessary for cross-boundary working.

Some Introductions

During 1997, five primary care joint commissioning projects were developed in the Dartford and Gravesham locality of West Kent Health Authority. Four of them were General Practice based and very similar in their approach and one was locality wide and very different in both scope and content. This chapter is a reflection on the experience of developing these projects. I have found it an extremely useful exercise in questioning the relationships and partnerships that developed and the processes that contributed to the work. Through this reflection it has been possible to identify those processes that worked well, and those that worked less well.

This locality is only one of four in our Health Authority area so it is important to try and understand what made this locality different from the others in attempting this work, and also to try and understand what were the magic combinations of events, people and processes that made the projects possible. The purpose is not to reduce what after all has been a complex process into simple steps and formulae, but to understand the key ingredients for success in these particular recipes if this is at all possible.

Some of the more general background information about West Kent Health Authority is described in Box 1, and more specific background information about the locality is described in Box 2.

Early in 1996, we began to develop a different approach to the involvement of GPs in commissioning, centered around each of the four localities. Previous to this the individual localities had various groups of either fundholding GPs or non-fundholding GPs who worked together, but separate from each other, to commission and advise on the development of local health services. Each group developed its own individual working arrangements and relationships with the Health Authority. In 1996 we set up four GP Joint Commissioning Groups (JCG) which drew both fundholding and non-fundholding GPs together with the Authority to look at services across the whole locality in an integrated and systematic way. At this stage Social Services were not involved.

Early in 1996, Dartford and Gravesham Joint Commissioning Group quickly established themselves as a core group of 7 GPs who were nominated by their peer group to represent them and who were keen to contribute. They were established under the auspices of the Local Medical Committee GP Sub-Committee and achieved early successes in reviewing and recommending developments in Palliative Care, Community Nursing, Adult Mental Health and Child & Adolescent Mental Health Services.

Box 1. West Kent Health Authority - some background information

West Kent Health Authority is a large Health Authority responsible for purchasing Health Care for over 950,000 people who live in the area. It is divided into four localities:

- Tunbridge Wells

- Maidstone

- Medway/Swale and

- Dartford and Gravesham.

These four localities were the original Health Authorities which merged in 1994 to form a single large Health Authority. In 1995 the former Family Health Services Authority which covered the whole of the county of Kent, split and merged with the two separate Health Authorities and on the first April 1996 the newly configured West Kent Health Authority was formally recognised.

The NHS in West Kent costs over £550 million each year. There are wide variations in the health of the populations. Across Dartford and Gravesham, and Medway and Swale localities there are higher levels of long term illness and higher rates of coronary heart disease and cancer. These localities are also associated with levels of relative deprivation. In West Kent there are:

- 527 General Practitioners

- 8 local NHS Trusts,

- 4 Community Health Councils,

- 9 Borough, District and City Councils,

- Kent County Council,

- Three areas for Social Services,
- A Unitary Authority in Medway fulfilling both District and County functions.

Box 2: Dartford and Gravesham Locality- Some background information

- Based on the 1991 census has a population of 220,000

- The Government Actuary Department identifies a population growth of 0.2%, which does not reflect projected growth associated with the Thames corridor developments.

- Within Gravesend and Northfleet there is an ethnic minority population of 10% of the locality population.

- Some local authority wards within Dartford, Gravesend and Northfleet are generally 'deprived' with higher proportion of residents who are unemployed, not owner occupiers, have no car, and live in overcrowded homes.

- One recent survey showed that in Dartford 31% of women over the age of 16 were smokers, (the highest levels in West Kent).

- The mental health admission rate for Dartford and Gravesend is higher than the other localities in West Kent.

The locality was served in 1997/8 by :

114 GPs, arranged in 37 practices, of which 15 were single handed. There were 12 full fundholding groups, 2 community fundholders and the remaining were non-fundholders. Thus, approximately 75% of the locality were fundholders and they were represented through "DAFT" (Dartford Active Fundholding Team), a group which met over a number of years to discuss fundholding issues.

Why this group of GPs?

What were the characteristics of this group of GPs that contributed to successful working, and made us think that it was worth investing time and staff to facilitate further developments ?

- *There was no huge gulf between fundholders and non-fundholders.*

  This was a significant factor. In other localities within West Kent, the introduction of fundholding status for some GPs had made apparent significant ideological differences - this was not true of the Dartford and Gravesham locality.

- *The GP Sub-Committee had continued to provide a focus for all GPs.*

  Over the past 6 years the ability of the locality based GP sub-committees to continue to provide a forum for debating GP issues in the face of ideological differences varied enormously. The Dartford and Gravesham Locality managed to do this, primarily because of their particular leadership abilities and styles.

- *A sense of shared values and purpose*

There was a shared view about the need for better local services, and a shared view about the areas most in need of attention and development. The core GPs were also committed to developing services locally, and saw a collaborative approach with other providers of health and social care as the key to achieving long term benefits in services. Fundholders who had used other providers outside the local NHS had seen this a short term approach and as lever to 'make local providers sit up and listen' to their concerns about the quality of some of the services.

The Next Steps

It was the success of the work of the GPs looking at the community nursing services that led to a project proposal to extend the work in a collaborative way with the local NHS Community Trust and Social Services. At the same time we were aware that the Kings Fund, with Department of Health funding and support, were facilitating a network of national pilots in joint commissioning. We felt that we had something to gain from and something to contribute to this work in that the locality project proposal was for practice based joint commissioning with GPs taking a key role.

The GPs had expressed a number of concerns that they felt the project should be able to address:

- firstly - that the management of the District Nursing Service was seen as constraining innovation rather than enabling;

- secondly - that roles within the wider primary health care team could be developed and enhanced, and duplication between them reduced;

- thirdly - that there would be closer working between the agencies driven by a better understanding and a greater valuing of each other's contributions;

- fourthly - that through this approach there would be development opportunities created for the local services in Practices.

The projects and their support

Under the umbrella title of 'COMPART' (The Community Partnerships Project), four geographically based development projects were identified based around GP Practices. They were self selecting in that the core GPs sounded out their colleagues about their commitment to participate in the development. Members of the primary health care team were identified to come together and form individual collaborative project groups. These groups involved practice nurses, community nurses, social service care managers, GPs and Health Authority staff ; their focus was on services for older people.

Initially a series of informal working lunches and structured workshops were held in order to identify hopes and aspirations, issues and problems, aspects of work that people wanted to protect and wanted to improve. The groups discussed the role of project manager and the kind of support that would be needed. Over a number of such meetings the groups began to identify the specific issues they wanted to focus on, including :

- joint assessment processes,

- aspects of occupational therapy services,

- the need for rehabilitation services,

- improving discharge and links with acute care,

- the need to provide better support and training for carers in the community,

- the need to look at blurring roles between different professions,

- looking at different management approaches.

How did we, at the Health Authority support this process? We had established an overarching project group to 'steer' the process. I chaired this group, as a Health Authority Director, able to commit my own staff to help and support each group. Other project group members included core GPs, the assistant area director for social services and a director of the Community Trust. I had identified a senior manager to project manage and co-ordinate the whole process and each project had a small budget to support local initiatives and training and support.

The remaining project was very different in its approach although it was part of the overall project management process for COMPART. It was developed from the work of the joint commissioning GPs on mental health services and was established as a locality wide group commissioning and purchasing the full range of mental health services for the whole locality.

The fundholders and the Health Authority 'pooled' their money in order to develop this joint approach. This required shared contracts, shared service specifications and service activity information and required the development of a shared service plan for the locality.

This project had its own Mental Health Board, involving GPs, the Community Trust, and Social Services. The GPs had already been actively involved in a lot of work looking at developing the work of the community mental health teams, the establishment of rehabilitation and crisis intervention services, and establishing policies for access to services. This project group relied on the Trust to carry forward the detailed work required. In many instances small groups got together to look at issues and solutions and involved Trust managers, clinicians, GPs, social services staff and public health consultant. The overall COMPART Project Manager also 'looked after' this project. I also chaired the Mental Health Board which had a very real business focus. It was linked very closely into the Authority's contracting approach and involved very detailed work on budgets and establishing appropriate processes which met fundholding regulations. The intention was to move steadily toward the inclusion of Social Services budgets as part of the funding resource, building upon the aligned decision making now in operation.

Learning to work together

There are a number of lessons that were learned through the project development process.

- The practitioners themselves made real achievements in getting to know each other better, exchanging information, understanding each other's language and working practices, and understanding each others' systems and organizations.

- The GPs began to understand more just how complex the systems are and began (over time) to realise the very real constraints in managing change and making a difference to services.

- The various Boards, (COMPART and Mental Health) began to understand the niceties of working together in that way, and getting to grips with personalities, disagreements, the 'ups' and the 'downs'.

- The Health Authority learnt to walk the 'tightrope' between directing the process, enabling ideas to grow and develop, relying on influence and persuasion, working in different ways through networks and groups.

Spanners in the Wheel

All was not smooth and straight forward, sweetness and light. It was very difficult to maintain momentum at times, particularly when achievements were slow to materialize and team members changed. One major set back occurred when having built up successful relationships with social service staff at Board level and at Practice level, there was a major re-organization within the Social Services Department which meant that area boundaries changed. Staff were at risk and having to apply for jobs, and there was a six month delay before new processes had worked themselves through and new team members were in place. Whilst everyone involved could understand the reasons for the problem there was a sense of real frustration which bubbled to the top on many occasions and which engendered a 'why bother' feeling expressed by many.

There were also some very real practical issues that had to be worked through. During the time when team members changed, people were very concerned not to set an agenda that new incoming team members could not then identify with and that of itself reinforced some of the feelings of frustration. Facilitation played a key role during that time.

But progress did pick up again, and all five projects resumed working on detailed project plans, service proposals and work programmes. All agencies involved - Health Authority, Social Services, GPs and Trust - recognized the importance of seeing the proposed changes through to fruition wherever possible.

Other major changes are on the horizon. Having 'seen through' Social Services re-organization, a merger of Community Trusts loomed on the horizon, and whilst this was unlikely to bring about job changes at practitioner level, it created an inevitable air of uncertainty at management level.

What this identifies is the chaotic environment in which we all now work, and that these dimensions have to be accounted for in managing any changes. If it isn't re-organizations, it's major changes in policy or changes in priorities determined by external factors, all buffeting the teams working at the 'coal face' trying to bring about continuity in working between and within different agencies.

The Importance of Leadership

The phrase 'leadership at every level' can be seen as a cliché and over used today. However it is both an appropriate description and an important one given the environment referred to in the previous paragraph.

- Leaders are needed at project group level to motivate, agree processes, seek innovations and new ways of doing things. They need to be able to facilitate, communicate and network. We hoped that leaders would emerge out of the group processes and that team members would identify those with the skills that most 'fitted the bill'. In reality some people needed a little 'nudging' and on reflection it might have been better to agree a more explicit process for identifying the leader earlier on in the establishment of the projects

- Similarly within the mental health project we needed to use the leadership within the local Trust to bring about change. The Director of Operations, the Clinical Director and the Head of Nursing were key roles. The changes required within the Mental Health Service were very complex and during the project development phase a management post for service development - a change facilitator - was identified and recruited to provide the link between the Mental Health Joint Commissioning Board and the services within the Trust.

- Leadership roles within Social Services were also key, providing the link between the local projects and the management of the wider organization and their resources.

- In my role as Director of Commissioning I provided the overall leadership for the project, with extremely able project management support. There was an early discussion at COMPART Board about chairing the Board and leading the project. It was very important to me personally and for the success of the project itself that the GPs endorsed my role. I personally felt a tension between directing and enabling. I was very comfortable as an enabler - providing a sense of purpose, ideas for the future, unblocking difficult problems, influencing and persuading, using my position to influence key people in other agencies and being able in my role to commit the Health Authority. I also felt comfortable dealing with conflict and performance internally within the Health Authority when needs dictated. However I felt a tension with a more 'directive' approach within the wider project, given that I had no formal authority within General Practice, the Trust or Social Services. The Mental Health Board recently had a workshop to agree its future work programme and one of the issues discussed was the style, format and working of the Board itself. The group decided that a more structured approach was required and gave me their 'permission' in a sense to provide the direction in a more structured and formal way if required.

- One of the key roles of various leaders within the project was to enable the link between the operational and strategic levels of the various organizations : the one needed to connect very clearly with the other. The local practitioners needed to be able to access decision makers at the strategic levels of the organizations. Otherwise good ideas would not come to fruition. In some respects the projects point to new organizational models. Working in these ways implies new informal organizations, those without boundaries, relying on networks and shared values and purposes to work together. This of itself requires different leadership skills.

Where Next?

The GPs and the Health Authority have been successful in taking the partnership concept one step further as a formal locality commissioning pilot. The Health Care Partnerships Project is one of 40 or so national projects bringing fundholders, non-fundholders and health authorities together to commission and purchase all services for the locality. Relationships and structures are still being developed but the joint commissioning projects are firmly within it. The COMPART Board continues to develop the Practice based partnership approach for services for older people and the Joint Commissioning Board for Mental Health continues its role of commissioning mental health services for the locality. Both feed into the structure of the Health Care Partnerships Project.

I believe that these approaches are very much what the future is made of, in line with the New NHS White Paper. Whilst statutory boundaries may or may not change we are building new organizational principles. These organizations have been described as 'virtual organizations', I think they are more tangible than that. I prefer the description of a 'Federal Approach' or 'Federal Model', using the analogy of Europe or the USA to describe the relative autonomy of the constituent players whilst also describing a unity and identity.

Over time the boundaries will blur, as people become more confident. The boundaries will blur between individual GP Practices, between professions, between statutory agencies, between general practice and community services and Trusts generally. But like the Federal Model, individual and relative identities and autonomy will remain.

The Social Services Director's Story

Towards a Seamless Service

Chris Williams
Director of Social Services,
Dudley Metropolitan Borough

Chris Williams heads up the Social Services Department in the largely urban borough of Dudley in the West Midlands. Like many other local authorities, Dudley has been rethinking the way in which it relates to health matters generally and to the Health Service in particular. Since he became Director some five years ago Chris has developed good personal and working links with senior NHS managers. But at primary care level progress has been largely opportunistic as Dudley has its fair share of GPs who are not able or not inclined to make links with social care. In this contribution Chris relates how it is still possible to make progress in such circumstances and gives some insight into the role of organisational leader in facilitating primary health and social care development.

Introduction

When I arrived in Dudley in 1993 there was little tradition of collaboration between social services and primary care, in contrast to what was already happening in some other places. At first I was concerned simply to promote greater collaboration in general. Even then it was clear that this was a crucial interface to develop. One of my tasks was to encourage experimentation, work out (with others) what was going well and then roll it out across the borough as best we could. Local authority elected Members were happy to support this approach as it fitted well with the Council's emerging agenda on "health and well being".

Dudley Borough in Context

Demographic Trends

The Dudley Metropolitan Borough was formed in 1974. It contains a mix of industrial and good quality residential areas. The 1995 OPCS mid-year estimates gives a total Borough population of 312,453 of which 249,890 are aged 15+. By 2001 the total population is expected to rise to 317,785 and the number of people in the Borough over the age of 65 will have risen to 50,220, which represents 15.8% of the local population and an 8.8% increase during the current decade. People from the black and minority ethnic communities make up 4.5% of the Borough's population and this is expected to rise to 5% by 2001.

Joint Commitment to Collaboration

Joint commitment to effective collaboration between Dudley Metropolitan Borough Council and Dudley Health Authority is clearly expressed through the strategic planning documents of both our organisations and their implementation. This is greatly assisted by the fact that the two organisations' geographic boundaries are co-terminous.

Thus the Health Authority document A Strategy for Health to the Year 2001, under 'Primary Care and Community', defines the strategic objective of the Health Authority as being "To improve the overall health and social well being of the people of Dudley through the provision of high quality local primary care and community health services."

Similarly, the objective of Dudley Metropolitan Borough Council is described in the Dudley Borough Agenda document, under 'Personal Well Being', as being "...to make sure that good quality services are available to safeguard the most vulnerable and disadvantaged residents in the Borough, and to provide services and community supports which will reduce the risks of residents not being able to care for themselves or others, while enabling people to reach their full potential."

These individually stated, but consistent objectives, are jointly expressed within Dudley's Community Care Plan. Personally I have spent many years promoting the concept of health as well-being rather than simply as medical intervention : from this it is unsurprising that I would want to encourage collaboration between health and social care services for the benefit of local people. We are all too well aware that people do not want a "health bath" nor a "social care bath" nor even a "psychological bath" they just want a bath.

Framework for Joint Working within Dudley Borough

The Joint Commissioning Board

In April 1996 the Joint Commissioning Board was formed with a membership consisting of executive representation from all relevant arms of the Local Authority, Health Authority and Council for Voluntary Service. Its terms of reference include :

> *"To establish a strategic framework and develop joint agency work at strategic levels by setting broad policy direction and deciding upon areas of joint priority action across community, health and social care services for children and adults against assessed needs over a one year, three year and longer term perspective."*

The Joint Commissioning Board, currently chaired by myself, is supported by a Joint Action Group which, in turn, is supported by a range of Joint Planning Teams and working groups based on client groupings.

Joint Planning

The joint planning structure's effectiveness in service development can be gauged through the increase from 12 jointly commissioned initiatives in March 1995 to 25 such initiatives in September 1996, when Dudley Social Services Department published its most recent Profile of Jointly Commissioned Initiatives and Joint Teams.

The current joint review of arrangements has highlighted a number of areas to which the joint agencies will be giving special attention during the next phase of our working together. These may be summarised as follows:

- development of mechanisms for achievement of a complementary system of purchasing and financial investment;

- development of compatible management information systems;

- mechanisms for tracking patterns of demand;

- mechanisms for identifying and responding to vulnerable areas of service development where investment is inadequate;

- effective involvement of service users and their carers;

- means by which to ensure the optimum use of opportunities presented by the existing legal framework.

Locally we have been very successful in developing collaboration with the Health Authority and Trusts, focussing on hospital discharge arrangements, multi-disciplinary assessments, local mental health teams, joint teams for learning disability services, continuing care agreements, and various jointly-commissioned initiatives. But we have been less confident about developing arrangements at the primary care level, probably because locally we have less experience in this area. Yet when local people want a service they will often go first to their GP for his or her advice.

The Dudley Projects

Background to Primary Care

Primary Care is for most people their first point of contact with health services in Dudley where over 90% of the health care being provided is entirely within a primary care setting. It is also the gateway to more specialised forms of health care and in many cases is the trigger for a social care assessment by staff of the Social Services Department.

Since 1993/1994, Dudley Health Authority has supported five GP locality commissioning groups. There is also an executive group comprising two practitioners from each locality and senior managers from the Health Authority.

The Health Authority has long been an enthusiastic advocate of active participation by GPs in the commissioning process as expressed in its purchasing plan. The range of issues GPs sought to take forward in 1998 included :

- the extension of working projects with the Social Services Department;

- further development of primary health care team working;

- the extension of integrated working with locality voluntary and statutory organisations;

- consideration of the potential of shared care schemes with other professionals in primary care;

- the extension of the transfer of selected services from hospital based provision into primary care;

- the encouragement of increased dialogue on a locality basis between professions, and increased involvement with voluntary groups and the general public.

At primary care level in Dudley concerns have focused upon the quality of assessments and the hospital/community interface. Research into health and social care received by older people and disabled people has frequently found that incomplete and delayed assessments result in the provision of inappropriate services.

Local experience is that, all too often, early hospital discharge is followed by a rapid deterioration of the person's health, leading to institutional or further hospital care. Often the major cause of such problems is lack of effective communication between agencies. It is hoped that work within Dudley Borough will not only enhance the quality of services to people recently discharged from hospital, but also clearly identify where the system is failing and identify steps which need to be taken to rectify the situation. Ultimately, it is hoped that the number of re-admissions will be significantly reduced, ensuring more effective use of both the inpatient and community resources.

Care received by older people and people with disabilities depends on effective co-operation between health and social services staff at grass roots level, but a framework of collaboration is also required at a more senior and strategic level. It seemed to me important to take a leadership role in encouraging the development of collaboration at primary care level. The idea was that locality projects, linked to existing GP Commissioning Groups, would provide the opportunity for social services staff and GPs alike to develop positive experiences which could then be used as models elsewhere in the borough.

My expectation was that the primary care collaboration work would provide experience of working together from which we could learn and roll out to other parts of the borough. More specifically I was looking for evidence of more appropriate referrals from GPs to Social Services, a more effective use of our and Health's resources, better planning and service design through working together, and a more positive approach to joint working.

Background to the Dudley Projects

Two projects embarked upon within Dudley have set out to address the above concerns. These pilots have three major elements :

- Social Services Department membership of a Locality Commissioning Group;

- a link social worker collaborating with a health centre within the same locality commissioning group;

- a joint project within a different locality focusing upon assessment and post discharge arrangements.

In developing these pilot projects, certain assumptions have been made:

- having a clearly identified link social worker improves liaison with the Primary Health Care Team;

- a link worker system enables social workers to participate in an effective joint assessment at an earlier stage in the development of problems;

- involving a social worker in the primary health care team enhances the continuity of care provided and greatly improves the knowledge of services which are available, which increases the likelihood of the most appropriate response being made to an individual's problem;

- there is a reduced likelihood of duplication of assessments.

1   The Beacon Commissioning Group Project

The Beacon Commissioning Group represents primarily non-fundholding practices although there are two independent fundholders on the group. There is also Health Authority and Social Services Department representation on the group, the latter from the Adult Purchasing Division, following an invitation in 1996 to standing membership of the group. Membership of this group has meant that, for the first time, the Social Services Department has had the opportunity to liaise with GPs at a strategic level, at least in terms of developing local services for one part of the Borough.

Membership has enabled social services operational staff to be involved in the development of the Health Authority Purchasing Plan and the Locality Resources Profile which clearly identifies how the Health Authority budget is spent locally. It is anticipated that future plans will include a social services perspective with the ultimate objective being the development of an effective and truly 'joint' local planning tool.

The group is well attended and provides an effective forum for the exchange of information as well as enhancing the relationship between GPs and the Social Services Department at a management level. It is very beneficial in encouraging mutual understanding of constraints, pressures and frustrations.

The initial outcomes can be summarised as:

- developing a partnership culture

- influencing decisions at a strategic level

- developing a framework for joint purchasing

- working together on specific policy and practice issues

2   Holly Hall Project

This Practice consists of two fundholding GPs who have a positive history of working closely with their local Social Services Department Area Office. They have a high percentage of older people on their practice list and have a significant number of hospital admissions and discharges. The decision to develop a project which focused on the administration of the hospital discharge procedure coincided with the development of a new discharge procedure.

The project has developed two strands - one being a fairly routine liaison between practice staff, including GPs and linked social workers, so enhancing the trust and communication between the two, and the other being a time limited and evaluated project focusing on the implementation of the hospital discharge procedures.

In preliminary discussions, it became apparent that the Practice staff and district social workers were experiencing similar problems in relation to discharge. Examples were:

- inadequate post discharge arrangements;
- no discharge arrangements at all for patients who had been treated privately, as they seemed to fall outside the protocols in place;
- no prior communication, even to GPs, of admissions or discharges;
- a significant number of re-admissions.

This part of the project is in its infancy as the revised hospital discharge procedure has not yet been implemented, but arrangements are in place for discharges to be tracked, quality of response by community staff to be evaluated, and client/patient experience of the whole process to be evaluated, with the help of researchers from a local university.

Impact on the Department

Key Principles

Implicit within the strategic objectives are key principles which mould my approach to joint working generally and to the interface between primary and social care in particular.

- ### The importance of Economic and Environmental Factors Affecting Dudley Borough

  The health and personal well being of Dudley Borough residents cannot be divorced from issues affecting the levels of social deprivation or opportunities for regeneration within the Borough. It is vital therefore that relevant agencies and departments of the Council are keyed into the concept of community care, with appropriate strategic planning taking place at a corporate level. The Dudley Borough Agenda, which is the Council's strategy for the next five years, is structured around four key themes - Economic Vitality, Personal Well-being, Lifetime Learning and Environment - rather than around traditional service departments. This provides for a more corporate role within the local authority : Personal Well-being covers Health and Social Care, Leisure, Safe Communities, and Social Cohesion and the Supportive Community, with objectives crossing departmental boundaries.

- ### Clear Vision and Leadership

  In accepting that there is a matrix of broad, structural issues at work within communities that may militate against achievement of the joint health and well being objective, it is vital that there should be clear vision and leadership in moving forward more specific agendas relating to health and social care. One aspect of my role has been to initiate projects at least in part to ensure that the Department is relatively "fresh". But having allocated the primary care development work to two managers I have expected and encouraged them to get on with it: to make the linkages, determine shared priorities with GPs and others, and then to make the case within the Department for any changes in purchasing priorities.

  There is a challenge associated with the management of potentially conflicting objectives between departments or agencies and ensuring effective communication and co-ordination within that network. In Dudley Borough, we find that maintaining a clear and consistent service user focus is a powerful principle in generating creative approaches to problem solving and corporate development within the context of community care.

- ### Prevention Is Better Than Cure?

  Implicit within the strategic objectives of both the Council and Health Authority is an emphasis on the development and maintenance of a healthy community. This makes it necessary to develop preventative strategies, avoiding or reducing factors known to have negative consequences, ensuring effective promotion of healthy lifestyles, and focusing on social care interventions that maximise potential for independence wherever possible.

- *Purchasing in Action*

During the past three years, Dudley Health Authority has invested in a series of developments to enable the purchasing of locally integrated and accessible health care services. Jointly, we wish to move towards the inclusion of social care services in this process, and many Primary Health Care Teams have developed a wide role in the planning and provision of services via GP fundholding and locality commissioning.

The Health Authority Purchasing Plan 1997/1998 states one of its objectives as being "to provide a support programme to local GP practices and attached staff, aimed at developing and maximising the skills available within the Primary Health Care Team".

The health service is currently examining the relationships between its primary and secondary care services and concluding that the way forward may be in the development of a unified commissioning service at a strategic level. This concept may usefully be extended to include social care services. Value to service users will involve professionals across relevant agencies collaborating to achieve agreed outcomes. This model of integrated care envisages one continuous care process or seamless service, which focuses upon service users and their needs, regardless of whether the need is for health care, social care or both, and combines effective interventions with opportunities for the service users to express choice.

The National Health Service and Community Care Act 1990 made Social Services responsible for co-ordinating community care services. The development of GP fundholding gave general practitioners greater authority to determine the patterns of care provided for their patients. In Dudley, locality purchasing groups were established which brought together groups of GPs (most of whom were non-fundholders) with representatives of the Health Authority (the principal commissioning body), to consider how local services should be shaped.

Future Developments in Dudley

Local Funding Issues

Underpinning the strategy of Dudley Health Authority and Dudley Social Services Department is the belief that access to health and social care services should be determined solely upon the basis of need.

Where primary health care is concerned, it is the aim of Dudley Health Authority to distribute funding on an equitable basis across the Borough, taking into account health care needs of the practice population with transparency and fairness, regardless of the commissioning status of GPs. It is likely that the framework for allocation of funding will be a capitation model, taking into account the differing health needs of the population. However, such developments must be understood within the context of financial pressures currently impacting upon Dudley Health Authority, which can be summarised as follows:

- The impact of phased pay awards to all major groups working with health services;

- The indexation of property values which has led to a sharp increase in the Trusts capital charge estimates in the West Midlands;

- The National Health Service Confederation estimate that a 3% growth is necessary annually to keep up with demographic changes, increased demand for emergency services, and changes in technology;

- The increasing cost of continuing care.

From the Social Services Department point of view, there is a significant commitment to the development of a Borough-wide policy to ensure the availability of social care support at all primary health care sites. However, it is not possible to identify an adequate resource at this time, with pressures on both the Department's base budget and Special Transitional Grant continuing to constrain growth.

The local financial position therefore makes it imperative that existing budgets and legal frameworks are used to maximum effect. Although the purchasing strategies of the Local Authority and Health Authority have historically been separate and discrete activities, there is an increasing acknowledgement that mechanisms to enable some pooling of resources would improve the value for money derived from current budgets.

Conclusion

So, health is not just about what the Health Authority does. Local Authority responsibilities and activities are key to the future well-being of our local people. The local joint commissioning projects are about developing positive experiences for the benefit of local people, but they also put into practice key messages about the role of the Local authority.

I have emphasised the need to engage at the highest corporate levels locally to ensure a positive outcome to achieving health and personal well being objectives. I have seen the primary care based joint commissioning work as pretty important in terms of departmental activities, and more so since the publication of the New NHS White Paper. I am very conscious that we are still near the beginning of what is an important new partnership at local level where we need to build upon the growing good will and translate that into better services for local people. The White Paper may offer some structural ways forward and I can envisage some top-slicing of social services budgets to the new Primary Care Groups.

In terms of service delivery and best value to service users and their carers, the importance of managing effectively the relationships between primary care and social care cannot, I believe, be over-emphasised.

The Joint Commissioning Officer's Story

Working Across Boundaries

Rachel Ayling
Joint Commissioning Officer
Merton, Sutton & Wandsworth Health Authority and Sutton Housing & Social
Services Department

Although she might not admit it Rachel Ayling is a boundroid. She is Joint Commissioning Officer in the London Borough of Sutton, a joint appointment by the local authority and the health authority. Like others in similar positions she has developed skills and acquired experience relevant to both health and social care. As is necessary in joint commissioning she is comfortable operating at the strategic level of the chief officers joint commissioning group as well as working with practitioners to design protocols for joint working arrangements. In this contribution she describes the situation in Sutton and how, in the period preceding the establishment of Primary Care Groups, the local Total Purchasing Project took part in efforts to develop greater integrated working at primary care level as part of an overall joint strategy for older people. Rachel describes her own role in these various developments: she indicates the complexity and sensitivity of the role as she seeks to achieve progress between sometimes reluctant partners.

This chapter describes the early stages of an initiative to provide a more integrated service for older people in a small outer London borough. Our work, which has been steered so far by a group of total purchasing GPs, is certain to develop over the next few years, as locality commissioning becomes a reality across our health district.

I will focus on the lessons we have learnt so far about the relationships between primary health care and social care services locally, and about methods for achieving change. I will also describe my own role, as a joint commissioning officer, and examine the potential of this kind of post to facilitate change.

Background

The Borough

This initiative took place in one of the smallest but most diverse London boroughs. The borough is located in wealthy commuter land on the fringes of London, but has pockets of deprivation and wards which share the characteristics of the inner city. The borough has a large elderly population, with 3,700 people (22% of the population) aged 85+.

It is served, along with two other boroughs to the north, by one of the largest district health authorities in the country. There is one acute hospital for the borough; community health services for older people are mainly provided by a single Community NHS Trust. The borough also has 37 GP practices, with 79 GPs, ranging from single-handed non-fundholding GPs to several waves of fundholders. In total, 10 have been fundholding and four of these belonged to a Total Purchasing Project (TPP).

The post of Joint Commissioning Officer

I have been employed since April 1995 to facilitate joint commissioning within the local authority's Housing and Social Services Department and the District Health Authority.

My post is jointly funded and jointly managed. I am accountable to a Joint Commissioning Group, chaired by the Director of Housing and Social Services, which determines my priorities and formally agrees my work programme each year. On a day to day basis, I am line managed simultaneously by an Associate Director (within the health authority) and the Head of Planning and Commissioning (within the local authority), and belong to their respective strategic commissioning teams. I have an office base in both organisations and divide my time equally between the two.

The post is thus designed to ensure that I work right alongside both health and social services commissioners. I have been expected to develop inside knowledge of both organisations and am, at least in theory, well placed to promote collaboration between them.

The post, which was originally funded for three years, has recently been made permanent, to reflect the growing importance of the health/social services partnership locally, as well as the developing central government agenda.

Joint Strategy Boards

The very existence of this post perhaps illustrates the priority given by both my employers to inter-agency collaboration. Before my appointment, the two agencies had developed a robust network of Joint Strategy Boards (JSBs) for each client group, reporting to the strategic Joint Commissioning Group (JCG) - *see Diagram A*. All of the JSBs included voluntary sector and user representatives as well as health and social services purchasers and providers. (However, no GPs were represented). All were tasked with developing a local Joint Strategy for their client group, in consultation with a wider group of users and stakeholders.

Diagram A

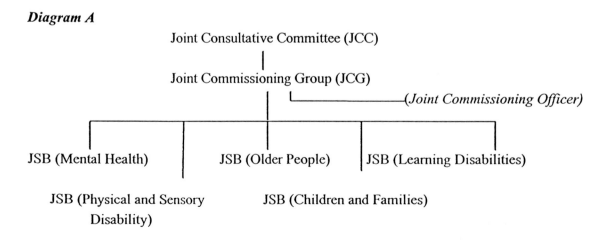

My own role has been to facilitate the work of the JCC and JCG, whilst simultaneously supporting the JSB for Older People to develop and implement a three year strategy for this client group.

Development of a Joint Strategy for Older People

The development of a Joint Strategy for Older People, starting in 1995, offered the opportunity for key agencies to articulate their vision for future service development, in consultation with a wide range of stakeholders. It also offered me, in my first year, a chance to establish relationships with each of the agencies concerned and to develop an understanding of how change might be achieved.

From the outset, the involvement of GPs posed a particular challenge. Whilst they obviously played a central role for older people themselves (and this was confirmed by those who took part in our consultation), GPs were almost the only professional group who were not directly represented on the JSB. Furthermore, at a strategic level, although two GPs attended the JCG, we had always suffered from the lack of a representative forum of GPs with which to engage.

A further complication was that the Family Health Services Authority (FHSA) did not merge with the District Health Authority (DHA) until that year. This resulted in the formation of an enlarged health authority, charged with the responsibility of developing a primary care led NHS . However, in the early stages, former FHSA staff were grouped within a separate Primary Care Commissioning Directorate. Attempts were made to synchronise their work with our own, but a truly co-ordinated approach was, at that stage, beyond our scope. It was not until another restructuring in the following year that the DHA was able to develop an integrated approach to commissioning, which combined primary care, secondary care and community care perspectives.

The development of our Strategy provided an opportunity for early dialogue with GPs. Two GPs attended our consultation meetings and a representative of the Total Purchasing Project subsequently joined the JSB. However, this hardly amounted to a strategic solution to the question of how to engage GPs in our joint planning. In spite of widespread recognition of the need to achieve seamlessness , our structures simply did not lend themselves to dialogue about what this might mean in practice.

The Joint Strategy for Older People

Our strategy, which was finally published in 1996, comprised:

- a statement of our shared vision;

- a detailed implementation plan, which specified the changes we wished to achieve over a three year period;

- a financial framework, which identified the resources currently spent on older people by both the health authority and local authority;

- a consultation strategy, describing how users would be involved in monitoring and reviewing the strategy.

The implementation plan encompassed a vast range of services, ranging from transport and information, to day care, domiciliary care and continuing care provision.

However, for the reasons described above, it was impossible to incorporate primary care developments or indeed to specify how the Health Authority's work to strengthen the role of GPs might impact on the range of other community services.

We recognised that further work would be needed to consult the wider constituency of GPs and prepare the ground before we could embark on major change. This would involve researching and exploring new ways of working, rather than launching into a more ambitious programme in the first three years.

The Implementation of the Strategy

Since 1996, I have continued to facilitate the work of the JCG, whilst simultaneously turning my attention to the implementation of our strategy. My day to day work has therefore involved a combination of strategic planning on the one hand, and project managing specific service changes.

The Context

My experience as a joint commissioning officer has been one of managing competing priorities, in a context of constant change. Before describing the outcomes it is perhaps important to list some of the contextual factors which have impacted on our work.

1   *Organisational Change*

Each of the agencies involved in our strategy has undergone almost unprecedented organisational change. This has resulted in changes at senior staff level, to the extent that few of those involved in approving our strategy are still in their posts.

Equally, there have been four changes in my direct line management in the last two years.

2   *Changing Priorities*

Both the JCG and JSB have been faced with a daunting set of competing demands since 1995, some of which have been triggered by central government, others by more local imperatives. It is important to note that whilst some of the priorities (e.g. the introduction of a new policy for NHS Continuing Care) have been of joint concern, others have applied to only one agency. Senior officers have therefore had to balance their own internal priorities with the ongoing joint agenda.

3   *Development of Locality Commissioning*

The general election, and subsequent publication of The New NHS White Paper, created   a somewhat uncertain climate for GPs themselves. Prior to the election, the DHA began to group local GPs into localities for the first time, but the composition of these groups was not finalised until late in 1997.

4   *Changing Financial Situation*

Both the local authority and health authority have also faced severe financial pressures, and both have had to make politically sensitive decisions about how to reduce expenditure. For the JCG - and myself as a joint commissioner - this has raised questions about how to strategically decommission and the extent to which this should also be a joint activity. In practice, the JCG has provided a useful forum for the confidential sharing of information, and early consultation between officers. However, it has not always proved possible to reach a consensus about proposed service reductions. The resulting tensions have at times diverted our attention from some of the tasks listed in our Joint Strategies.

Achievements

Our Implementation Plan - which listed our tasks and timetable, and also specified the agency responsible for taking the lead in each case - has provided a more or less robust framework for developing older people's services, in spite of this changing landscape.

After the first two years, it is possible to report that many of our targets have been achieved, or even exceeded. All of the following, for example, can be described as joint initiatives in that they have been planned by the two purchasing authorities and either funded by both agencies, or pump-primed from Joint Finance :

- The appointment of a Joint Training Officer, and the delivery of multi-agency training in the new Continuing Care arrangements to 180 professionals across the borough;

- The development of a range of jointly provided services in the community. These include shared intensive care packages for those assessed as needing exceptionally high levels of care, and a new community based rehabilitation scheme;

- A new hospital discharge policy, and intensive joint work to alleviate pressures on the local hospital over the winter of 1997/8. This includes a new scheme to prevent clinically unnecessary admissions to hospital, by providing fast-track assessments and services for patients attending the local Accident and Emergency Unit and GP surgeries;

- The introduction of therapy services to the borough's day centres, through the establishment of a multi-agency rehabilitation team;

- A new practical care service, a community transport strategy, and other preventative services in the independent sector.

Ingredients of Success

Such successes can perhaps be attributed to the following factors:

1   Our tradition of **jointly developing services** on a borough-wide basis, using centralised budgets or specific funds;

2   A culture of **team work** at middle management level, and opportunities to meet regularly on the JSB;

3   Success in **obtaining external funds**, and a willingness to use these in an opportunistic way;

4   A **realistic set of objectives**, which assumed that no additional resources would be available and that changes, in some areas, would need to be incremental;

5   A **commitment to the strategy**, and determination to regularly monitor against the expressed objectives.

To this I could add the existence of my own post, to project manage specific changes within the framework of the strategy - I shall return to this subject in the final sections.

The TPP's Integrated Care for Older People Initiative

The TPP's involvement in the development of our strategy meant that they were well placed to lead our exploratory work in relation to the primary health care/social care interface. Their proposal was for a research project, followed by pilot work at practice level, designed to test new ways of working.

Their strong interest in collaborating with the borough, the offer of leadership from their management team, and their success in achieving radical change in other service areas, suggested that these practices could provide a seed bed in which to test some ideas.

Description of the Project

The project's development so far can be summarised as follows:

Phase One
Appointment of a researcher for a six month period, to consult with users and practitioners from four TPP practices, using a combination of methods (including interviews and focus group discussions).

Phase Two
Establishment of a steering group, chaired by the Chief Executive of the TPP, and comprising an Assistant Director from the Social Services Department, an Associate Director from the Health Authority, and myself.

Phase Three
Establishment of multi-agency project groups in three general practices, each including a GP, charged with the task of identifying the obstacles to joint working and proposing and piloting solutions.

Phase Four
Development (by one project group) of a GP/Social Services Agreement, to be piloted in one practice and then offered to other practices as a possible model.

Interim Conclusions

The work of the research consultant, and messages received from each of the project groups, have given the JSB a much better understanding of the pattern of services in the community, how they inter-relate, what working relationships have evolved in different practices, and how they impact on service users. The emerging issues can be summarised as follows:

Multi-disciplinary team work

At GP practice level, there are networks of professionals attempting to work together, their success being determined largely by local personalities and ad hoc arrangements, rather than formalised systems. Poor communications, lack of understanding of each other's roles, and the absence of formally agreed procedures (e.g. for multi-agency assessments) are amongst the factors which militate against team work. As a result, we are probably duplicating each other, and missing the opportunities afforded by holistic approaches, whilst also causing unnecessary disruption for service users.

Multi-Agency Assessments

Whereas users complain that they are assessed too many times, those responsible for purchasing services often complain that they are not given the right information, or sufficient information, or that they are faced with different professional assessments which contradict each other. The introduction of new criteria for NHS Continuing Care has exposed these existing weaknesses in our community care assessment processes, and has led assessors themselves to request easier access to each other and improved documentation. We need to acknowledge, however, that any such improvements would be taking place against a background of renewed anxiety amongst professionals about their role in rationing services. For social services assessors, such tensions have been exacerbated by recent legal cases, reminding them of the tight statutory framework within which they operate.

Eligibility for services

The explicit or implicit tightening of criteria for services is by far the most significant source of tension between social and health care professionals at primary care level. This, of course, reflects the dynamics at senior manager level, even where conscious attempts are made to mask the difficulties. In the worst instances tensions over resources may be impacting on professionals' willingness to work together, even where, ironically, joint work has the potential to lead to less duplication and more cost-effective solutions.

Fragmentation

The TPP's researcher, describing our jigsaw of proposed and actual services, warned of the dangers of increasing fragmentation. Our success in developing new, more specialised services in the community has not always been matched by careful marketing of these to the professionals responsible for making referrals, or proper consideration of how seamlessness can be ensured. We need to avoid inadvertently introducing even more assessments to determine users' eligibility for services, waits as users are transferred between services, lack of staff continuity (one of the elements most valued by users themselves) and more or less open rivalries between service deliverers.

Service Delivery

Finally, we need to address the relationship between district nurses, home carers, occupational therapists and other service providers within the home setting. Whilst this issue could be partly resolved at the assessment stage, our research highlighted the continuing importance of home care organisers in monitoring packages of care, making day-to-day adjustments, and meeting with district nurses on a case-by-case basis. Such communication was seen by nurses as far more difficult when an unknown private agency, rather than the more familiar local authority home care service, was providing care.

In acknowledging the valuable work so far undertaken at the grass roots by our project groups, some of these issues clearly require action at a more strategic level.

Yet, as we begin to consider the wider questions - such as whether further changes are needed to the structure and locations of services, or to the way services are purchased - we are likely to be challenged by the absence of obvious mechanisms for achieving change. On the one hand, the relative autonomy of general practitioners, their responsibility for budgets, and their influence over community health services, mean that even quite basic changes in working practice need to be negotiated and agreed at individual surgery level. On the other hand, for the local authority, some of the issues described above can only be addressed strategically, with the involvement of senior officers and politicians.

This area of work, perhaps more than any other, therefore raises questions about the right process for achieving change. Success might depend on getting the balance right between top down planning and bottom up development work. To this can be added the importance of good timing; we need, on the one hand, to seize opportunities when they arise, and on the other hand to be mindful of other planned events which might, if not foreseen, eventually overtake us.

My Role as Joint Commissioning Officer

In exploring my own contribution to the work so far, it seems important to emphasise the similarities between my own day to day work, and that of my colleagues. As a member of two commissioning teams, I am aware that most of my colleagues are working in the same multi-agency context, forging relationships with their counterparts, and experimenting with different processes for achieving change. Equally, the skills I have acquired - including the ability to seek common ground, and to find imaginative solutions where agencies' interests appear to clash - are also essential to their roles.

On the other hand, my position on the boundary between the two authorities is clearly unusual. In conclusion, I will therefore describe some of the challenges and opportunities afforded by my post.

Practical Issues

In very practical terms, the need to keep track of both authorities' commissioning intentions, internal priorities, and changing statutory obligations, has had additional implications for my workload. Moreover, there has been the pressure of handling two in-trays, relating to two secretaries, juggling two offices, transporting papers between two locations, and being invited to double the usual number of internal meetings! For my line managers, there have also been challenges: it has sometimes been difficult to manage my workload or to achieve complete agreement about what should be given priority.

For all my colleagues, however, I am hopefully a rather useful resource, precisely because of my nomadic existence. I am constantly asked for information about the respective organisations' structures and hierarchies; I can usually signpost colleagues to the right person in the opposite authority, and quickly advise about who should be invited to particular meetings. External agencies, too, can sometimes save two phone calls by contacting me: an example is that voluntary organisations use me to enquire about both sources of statutory funding.

Speeding up the Process

It is a truism that joint planning is time-consuming work. Because of the time it takes for officers to reach each other, decision-making (even about a relatively simple matter, like the award of a small Joint Finance grant) can be slow. My physical presence in both headquarters certainly reduces the time it takes to complete certain tasks. In drawing up an agenda for the JCG, or putting together a joint bid for external funds to meet a tight deadline, or drafting a protocol for a new joint service, I am aware that I can usually represent the views of both authorities and sometimes spare them the task of consulting on several drafts! Equally, I find that colleagues sometimes test plans with me, to try to anticipate the reaction of the other authority before embarking on more formal consultation.

Staying on Course

It is clear from the above overview that both the JSB and JCG have had to juggle competing priorities, and constantly respond to new demands. As the borough's only Joint Commissioning Officer, I have had almost no scope to set the agenda ; indeed, it is debatable whether even my most senior colleagues are ever quite free to do this! On the other hand, the very existence of my post, my personal commitment to joint work, and our determination to regularly monitor progress against the original objectives, have perhaps helped to keep the work on course.

Project Management

Unlike most of my colleagues on the JSB, I do not have responsibilities for managing either staff or budgets, and have thus been relatively free to play a developmental role.

My approach has been to lend my support and time to new initiatives, whilst being careful to respect others' roles and ensuring that decisions are not taken out of the hands of those directly responsible. This has frequently involved finding sponsors at senior level, and ensuring that they support and 'own' the work by keeping them properly informed. My relatively easy access to the most senior tiers, through the JCG, has perhaps helped in this respect.

Working in a Matrix

The experience has been one of working in not one, but several organisational matrices. Whilst this has stretched my skills of diplomacy, and sometimes felt extremely uncomfortable, the reward has been in the sense of acquiring a unique perspective. Within the hospital, for example, I have developed a strong relationship with the social work team, balanced with an equivalent relationship with the Trust's staff. This has undoubtedly helped me to understand and communicate the 'true' reasons for so-called blocked beds and to understand why there might be different versions of this 'truth'.

Moreover, my role on the JCG, combined with the 'hands on' work to implement the srategy, has meant that I constantly move up and down vertical hierarchies, monitoring and observing the work of practitioners and passing on my observations to strategic commissioners. For example, it was only by attending multi-agency training sessions, and witnessing the discussions between front-line staff, that I recognised the gap between our rhetoric and the reality concerning so-called 'multi-disciplinary team work' at practice level.

I thus find myself moving around a complex network of agencies, trying to use my 'neutral' position to understand the dynamics both within and between organisations. In the course of these journeys, I am constantly struck by the way the quality of relationships - between individuals and between agencies - impact on the way services develop.

Maintaining Trust

Equally, it is probably true that my ability to achieve change depends largely on maintaining the trust of my immediate colleagues. Even after three years, individuals may sometimes hesitate to share a confidential document with me, because of my closeness to 'the other side'. My own position of course fluctuates along with the relationship between my two employers, and as suggested above, there have moments of real tension over the last three years. At such times, I have sometimes been guilty of sacrificing my own objectives, and those of the joint strategy, for fear of pushing too hard. It is certainly true that a few aspects of the strategy have so far been shelved, to await more opportune times. However, with hindsight I am convinced that it would not have been possible, in the circumstances, to move any faster and that my 'invisible' work to maintain the relationship may have been more appropriate than a very single-minded drive to meet deadlines.

Providing Objectivity

On the other hand, difficult negotiations (for example, about the de-commissioning of long term care beds) may occasionally have been eased by the existence of my post. My role, in such instances, has been to act as a fact finder , modelling the likely impact of bed reductions, and trying to draw objective conclusions about whether a cost shunt will occur. The search for hard data has sometimes been an illusive one, but the struggle to retrieve data from incompatible systems, and indeed to encourage the development of shared information systems, has become an essential part of my role.

Those directly involved in the negotiations have hopefully been better informed as a result of such work. However, successful resolution has been mostly due to their own skills and commitment to the partnership; my role, in this sense, is always far easier than theirs.

Ensuring Continuity

Finally, one more unexpected advantage of my post may be worth mentioning. Staff changes over the period of the Strategy have interrupted the relationship between the two authorities at strategic level, to the extent that the JCG has been attended by a succession of different staff over the last three years. My role, in this context, has sometimes reverted to one of messenger, communicating news about forthcoming changes, trying to interpret their implications, briefing new senior officers, providing background information and generally trying to minimise the effects of the constant disruptions.

As part of this work, I have sometimes felt it necessary to 'sell' the Joint Strategy for Older People to incoming staff, who might otherwise have lost it in the rather thick pile on their shelf.

Conclusions

As far as the primary care/social care initiative is concerned, the main outcome of our work so far has been a much improved understanding of the dynamics within primary health care teams, and the relationships between them and their social services colleagues. Our model GP/Social Services Agreement reflects this understanding, and the process of developing it has in itself been an informative one.

The introduction of the Agreement, and the requirement to monitor its implementation, has provided a pretext for social care and primary care professionals (including a GP) at one practice to meet regularly, to discuss their operational difficulties, and to introduce practical changes on an experimental basis. So far, this has led to some tangible improvements (for example, in referral procedures and the timeliness of professionals' responses to each other) as well as improving the participants' own experiences of team work within that practice. The Agreement will now be 'rolled out' to other TPP practices, and then introduced to other GPs as a possible model.

On a personal level, the insights I have gained are probably unique, precisely because I am required to be completely objective. The success of the next phase of the work may partly depend on my own success in communicating what I have learnt. However, we will also need to work hard to identify new processes for achieving change, in the light of the formation of Primary Care Groups and the requirements of the government's White Paper.

My role has always entailed a willingness to be flexible and to appreciate that many different factors may influence the pace of change. All the current indications are that the landscape is once again about to change, with new implications for the GP/Social Services interface. It is to be hoped that this will result in real improvements for older people themselves.

Postscript

Where are they now?

The reflections featured in these accounts of partnership between primary and social care were written in 1998, before Primary Care Groups were established and before the Government decided to introduce a duty of partnership into new arrangements for the NHS and local government. This postscript provides details of the authors, showing what role they are playing in 1999 as the new arrangements come into place.

Rachel Ayling

Rachel remains in her post as Joint Commissioning Officer for Merton, Sutton & Wandsworth Health Authority and Sutton Housing & Social Services Department. She is involved in writing a joint investment plan for older people as part of the Health Improvement Programme.

George Blackburn

George is currently seconded to the management of learning disability services in North & West Wiltshire where he continues to work across the health and social care boundaries.

Jim Rogers

Jim continues to work as a social worker/care manager for Knowsley Social Services in Huyton on Merseyside. He is still attached to the two GP practices mentioned although contact had to be temporarily suspended through part of last year due to staffing problems. He is a member of the Primary Care Team in each practice.

Stephanie Stanwick

Stephanie has recently been appointed as Chief Executive of Dartford and Gravesham Partnerships Primary Care Group. This is a Primary Care Group that wants to become a first wave Primary Care Trust.

Alasdair Thomson

Alasdair is now the Chairman of Dartford, Gravesham and Swanley Healthcare Partnerships Primary Care Group and he continues to work collaboratively with his counterparts in health and social care services. He is also involved in local Health Improvement Programmes through his role in the PCG.

Chris Williams

Chris continues in his post as Director of Dudley Social Services in the West Midlands. He has been involved in discussions about social services representatives on Primary Care Group Boards who have appointed locality managers to each of the PCGs in his area. He is currently playing an active role in the team developing health improvement.

Other Relevant Reading

Poxton R *Primary Health and Social Care Partnerships: lessons from joint commissioning* King's Fund 1999

Robinson J, Poxton R Health and Social Care Partnerships In: Klein R (Ed) *Implementing the White Paper, Pitfalls and Opportunities* London: King's Fund 1998

Myles S, Wykes S, Popay J, Scott J, Campbell A, Girling J. *Total Puchasing and Community and Continuing Care: lessons for future policy developments in the NHS* London: King's Fund 1998